FRED'S STORY

A Trauma Recovery Workbook

RUTH LONG, LPC-S

Copyright © 2014 Manitou Communications, Inc.

1701 Gateway, Suite 349

Richardson, TX 75080

Phone: 1-800-572-9588, FAX: 972-918-9069

rossinst@rossinst.com,

www.rossinst.com, www.manitoucommunications.com

A pdf copy of the Fred's Story Workbook can be downloaded for free and used without further permission from www.rossinst.com.

Library of Congress Cataloging-in-Publication Data:

Ruth Long

    Fred's Story

ISBN 10: 0-9815376-4-2

ISBN-13: 978-0-9815376-4-1

1.   Child Abuse   2. Child Neglect   3. Recovery

Illustrations by Sharon Morris

FOREWORD

Ruth Long has worked with me in my Trauma Program in Dallas, Texas. The people who come for treatment there have many different mental health problems and most have had traumatic and stressful childhoods. They have experienced physical abuse, sexual abuse, family violence, neglect, loss of primary caretakers, and extremely dysfunctional family dynamics. Their mental health problems include depression, dissociative disorders, posttraumatic stress disorder, substance abuse, self-mutilation, eating disorders, borderline personality disorder, panic disorder and obsessive compulsive disorder.

Ruth understands survivors of childhood trauma very well. She understands the self-blame and self-hatred that come from being treated like you don't count, like an object, like a burden and disappointment, or like you're invisible. These messages are ingrained in the child's head over and over for years, through the speech, actions and attitudes of their caretakers. Fred would understand.

In *Fred's Story*, Ruth captures the conflicts and problems of the abused and neglected child in a vivid yet simple fashion. It is a child's story for adults, one that can be read by children as well. Setting the story in a circus, and in the suffering of an elephant, is a wonderful way to draw the reader in, to create empathy, and thereby to teach at both an intellectual and an emotional level.

When I arrive at the Trauma Program in the morning, and

Ruth is there in the nursing station writing her notes, or preparing for a therapy session, I sometimes ask, "How's Fred today?"

I feel like Fred is a real elephant and a real person, someone I know, someone whose struggles I have watched and experienced. When you read *Fred's Story*, I think you will feel the same way. It is a story of trauma, suffering, healing, hope and recovery. Fred's attachment to his chain is a moving and subtle dramatization of the conflicted, ambivalent attachment to the perpetrator experienced by many abused and neglected children. The workbook that accompanies *Fred's Story* is a set of exercises that capture much of the work of recovery. I think that survivors will find them useful, and will appreciate knowing that someone else – Fred – has gone through what they have gone through, and come out the other side.

Colin A. Ross, M.D.
Dallas, Texas

CHAPTER ONE

The story of Fred is somehow incredibly difficult to embrace as what one would call "true," "real," or "possible," for it defies the rational mind and begs the audience of the imaginary. Yet, despite this seemingly absurd occurrence, the story of Fred is all too real. Fred has a story to tell and has chosen to share it with you in this special moment.

The story of Fred begins at the county circus ground where Egbert and Eloise anxiously await the arrival of their precious first-born baby. . . elephant. Acrobats, clowns, groundskeepers and the like are all pulled in to the eager excitement as the, both proud and nervous, parents await their newborn's arrival.

The anxious parents find themselves pacing around the various tents trying to ease the gnawing suspense. Egbert and Eloise have too much time alone with their thoughts, and rumination brings them to the difficult memory of last week's meltdown over naming the imminent offspring. Traditions were to be honored, rules to be followed, and these new upcoming parents were well convinced of what terrible things could happen to them if there was any hint of noncompliance. They reasoned among themselves that if they were to be parents and expect their little one to do what was expected, wouldn't they be sending a disturbing mixed message if they refused to follow their elders' mandates? Back as far as they could remember, from one ancestor to the next, there was a firm but unspoken rule about the names to be assigned to any elephant child.

There was a sense of sacredness to this rule although it was rarely disclosed in public. Everyone just knew, it was not to be challenged. Egbert and Eloise, though not always enamored with their given names, were nevertheless secretly relieved that they were at least safe from social bias since the "E" rule was blindly applied by their dutiful parents. But now they were parents to be and often entertained the endless possibilities of potential names that they could select as a sign of their blessed position. I mean, what was wrong with the letter "B" or "J" as the initial letter in an elephant's labeling? OK, the assumed rationale was the obvious correlation that elephant starts with an "E". . . but why did that matter so much?!

Oh, and what a meltdown it was! Eloise was the first to get her trunk all up in the air about the issue. Egbert initially was annoyed at his partner's desires to be different, but he too was growing weary of this "following the pack" mindset. After all, maybe his partner was right. . . and who's in charge here anyway! The strange thing, that both pioneers couldn't quite understand about the odd intensity of this current struggle, is that they were the end of the line in their family. All of their relatives had either passed from old age or were shamefully destroyed by malicious hunters or plagues.

So, who was gonna find out if they "broke the rules" or not? Still, the haunting contemplation carried shame, and even the thought of defiance created such internal chaos that Eloise had started to develop severe health problems. There were the ongoing chest pains, not to mention the chronic upset stomach. The sicker she got, the madder Egbert got that his partner had to suffer so, just for wanting the right to name her own child her way.

Fearing the effect all this stress might have on the little body inside, Egbert and Eloise decided to put an end to the turmoil and just stand their ground, despite the lure of the past calling out to them to join the ranks at any cost. The decision was made. . . the newborn would be named "Fred." (OK. . . it has an "E"in it. . . just in case. . .) . . . and "Fredreeka" if a girl. . . (triple "E's". . . Eloise's sly way of giving the girl the upper hand. . . just in case. . .).

CHAPTER TWO

"Honey, . . HONEY!!. . . (a little help here!). . . I think it's time!!!!"
It was time. The long awaited child had announced it was tired
of the cramped quarters. "Fred" was coming, ready or not, to join
the outside world. Lucky for "Fred," the male elephant father was
a little calmer than the shell-shocked human counterpart. Eloise
felt the strong support of her lifelong companion gently coaching
her on her breathing. He was with her every step of the way.
Hiding his concerns bravely from the view of his beloved, Egbert
was able to distract himself from the reminders of his dear one's
recent bout with some frightening symptoms. He focused solely
on his best friend who had a challenging ordeal in front of her.
How proud of Eloise, Egbert was. Her focus remained on her
birthing child and doing everything within her power to make his
journey successful. Everything seemed to be going so well. It

had to. Who could tolerate any other fate?

Without even a decent warning, this glorious scene of triumph turned to the most bitter of tragedies. Fred was seconds from arrival when Eloise simply grew coldly quiet. Time seemed to freeze in deference to the abrupt horror. Egbert called Eloise's name, praying that there would be a response, hoping that what appeared to be, was merely a false alarm. No response was given, but Fred could not wait. His arrival could not be met with joy and celebration. Contempt was all Egbert could muster up. At the sight of his "murderous son," Egbert recoiled in resentful rage. . . and turned and walked away. . . for good.

Contrary to the hearty welcome, the warm embrace, or even the basic care given to every newborn, Fred spent his first several hours alone and abandoned.

Fred would never experience his mother's comfort and nurturing. What he would experience, in ample supply, was his father's neglect and disdain. Unwilling to face his own vulnerability, Egbert refused to ever feel that helpless again. There had to be a way to fix this, to have prevented this. Someone must be responsible. Was it him, the father, who was being punished for straying from the edicts of past ages?. . . NO! Absolutely not! He could not bear such a conclusion. . . He loved her. . . He couldn't face the world without her. . . It couldn't be his fault! Then who? Who was to blame?. . .

That's when it seemed that a more palatable culprit became oh so obvious. It was that selfish, brat of a baby! Egbert tried to choke out the word "son" but that was too personal. . . too connected to him. Better the villain remain disowned. Did that thing think he was more important than his own mother?. . . What right does he have to live and my soulmate die? How could he kill the one who carried him all that time?! It had to be him, there was no one else there.

For years Egbert lived in his own torment. He blamed his own flesh and blood for choosing to be born, a process that Fred had absolutely no control over. This mattered little to this grieving bitter father. Fred had no one and nowhere to plead his case. He was too young to know that he even had a case to plead. All Fred knew was that he was incredibly alone.

The years to follow would only compound and confuse this both naive and innocent little mind.

CHAPTER THREE

Circus directors tend to place high priority on. . . containment. Leaving the circus was in all practical points of consideration. . . taboo. Suffice it to say that such grand and lofty ambition was "frowned upon." And in suspected form, this circus director was not about to allow for any more losses. If losing Eloise wasn't bad enough, the subsequent break from reason in the bereaving spouse was the proverbial straw that broke the camel's back. Never before had the director seen such a profound reaction from one of his beasts. Egbert never performed again. His moods were unpredictable and his behaviors just could not be trusted. Fearful of any further costly mishaps, the director made certain he would not lose another act. No one within a circumference of five miles missed this bellowed order requiring that Fred, from this day forth, be chained to a cemented post at all times when not practicing or performing.

. . . Standard practice. . . not illegal confinement. . . ?. . . That's the way everybody did it. . . Fred was property. . . Fred's life purpose was to make money for others. . . and assets better pay off or they may not be deemed worth taking up space in the cruel world around them! Fred's needs were just second rate inconveniences. . . . Could it be that Fred's self-declared owners blamed Fred as well for the loss of his mother (and father). How could it not seem to matter that Fred was the one who had really received the most potent of blows in these losses? . . . Could it be that Fred, from his earliest moments, was beginning to come to the same conclusion about his parents' demises?

The days passed on, and the chain to the metal ankle band obediently fullfilled its directive. Fred, however, was the typical youngster who had an endless supply of energy but no patience for things standing still. He was so curious. He just had to explore his surroundings. Friend or foe. Fred was never completely sure. How confusing this all was! The chain did bring structure and companionship, but it also brought bondage and pain. Fred had no-one. Now, at least, he had something.

Fred did not like the chain at all at first, but over time, the chain became Fred's one constant. It was the only thing Fred could feel connected to. You see, although the chain brought Fred much misery and domination, it was still something he could finally attach to and call home. From the time Fred was found curled up next to his departed mother's body, Fred would find a different comfort zone. It was a distraction from the stifling and inescapable loneliness, for it was the one thing Fred could always count on to be there for him.

CHAPTER FOUR

Noise, Noise, Noise! There's so much racket in the hustle and bustle of Circus Days! These were the days when mistakes were just NOT an option! It's certain that all the practice in the world can make for a mighty fine show but never the perfect one. Fred would cringe with each performance trying to get everything just right, hoping for his trainer's ultimate applause and approval. Such was never to be the case for Fred, he would not get the opportunity to experience such an appropriate reward for his effort. No matter how hard he tried, there was always. . . something the trainer got mad about. If only Fred could figure out what he was doing wrong, his trainer would treat him better.

Fred's biggest frustration came one day when he did a spectacular job to the ecstatic audience and thought, for sure, this would be the time he would gain his trainer's love. As Fred's gaze turned from the cheering crowd to his trainer's face, he was confounded by his trainer's look of disgust. Why?? Fred screamed in silent agony. What did I do?? . . .

Failure. . . after failure. . . after failure, Fred began to wonder if anything he did was ever good enough. And maybe, it wasn't about what he did at all, but it was about who he was.

"Maybe there is something terribly wrong with me," Fred muttered," if my trainer can't be pleased with me even just once!"

Fred's anger had nowhere else to go so he aimed it straight at himself. His mind began racing with a plethora of personal self-slams such as "Stupid!". . . "Moron!". . . "Idiot!". . . just to name a few. He even started to make up words to diss himself when the old words didn't seem to have the same juice anymore.

"No wonder I'm alone," Fred thought. "Who would want to be around someone so awful as me!"

Strangely, the more Fred berated himself, the less he was focused on the loneliness and disappointment. He could then even rationalize that it was better that he was alone so no one would get too close and discover his embarrassing secret. The thought of further rejection terrified Fred, and it somehow felt safer to keep everyone at a distance.

"After all, it's just not right," Fred thought," to make people get so mad all the time so they can't be happy. They definitely are better off without me."

In the world outside, Fred believed he was finally learning where he belonged. It wouldn't be long, though, before he discovered there could be a different world inside his head, and Fred would be off to explore it.

CHAPTER FIVE

Flying Fred the Elephant

The rocket was seconds away from launch. The countdown had begun.   10. . . 9. . . 8. . . 7. . . (we pause this countdown for a commercial break. . . I mean. . . for a technical difficulty. . . I mean. . . CRAP!. . .). There's something wrong with the launching field, sir. Fred was furious! He had planned and prepared for a perfect launch but the shoddy equipment was almost more than he could stand. Again, the chain was tangled around the pole and Fred was stuck, trunk in the dirt. . . Okie dokie. . . let's do the usual reverse revolution and get this show on the road!. . . All righty, then....the clock is reset and the first flying elephant poises for lift off. He hears the countdown begin again, thanks Houston for the timely save, and prepares for orbit. . . 10. . . 9. .

. 8. . . 7. . . 6. . . 5. . . 4. . . 3. . . 2. . . 1. . . BLAST OFF!!

Fred loved to pretend he was on an important secret mission to a different time and place. He was sure this mission required someone with supernatural vision and strength, and in this world, he had it all! When he played the superhero, he could be anything he wanted to be, and go anywhere he wanted to go. The best part of every flawless mission was the anticipation of the return flight. Here he could dream of the awaiting ecstatic and cheering crowds who were grateful beyond words for their very lives. But wait. . . Fred could not think of his imminent but future glory, he MUST keep his mind on the mission at hand. This mission was even more challenging than the last, and Fred was determined to gain victory for one and all!

Fred's utmost enemy and villain was on the prowl and loved nothing better than wreaking fear and destruction upon those in his way. Fred would not be foolish enough to underestimate his adversary. Using every mental and material weapon at his disposal, Fred had a plan. Wait for it. . . Wait for it. . . Almost there. . . Wait for it. . . Wait for. . . SNAP. . . Got 'cha!!!

Fred circled around his sequestered foe and delivered his own version of reading the degenerate suspect "his rights.". . . Fred's mission was finished and then there was only one thing left to do. . . prepare for his return flight.

Fred's heart began to beat at an amazingly accelerated pace. All he could think about now was his welcoming audience. They would be so thrilled at his arrival. Fred was so excited about the return trip, he opted to ride home in hyper drive.

Although this rate of speed had a history of some less than pleasant side effects, Fred (feeling a bit indestructable) ordered the adjusted speed nevertheless. There were some fleeting reminders of the last pre-flight fiasco, but. . . who worries about that miniscule little detail anyway!. . . Fred just couldn't wait!

Hyperdrive engaged, sir. Lift off in 5. . . 4. . . 3. . . 2. . . 1. . . (Uh. . . nothing happened, sir). . . Well, DUH!, Fred retorted. (Sir. . . I don't mean to bring this up now. . . but. . . I told you so!!!)

Fred was beside himself, there were parades to watch, people to be worshipped by. . . how could this keep happening?? All right! Can we make the flight in standard drive? (I think so, sir). . . Then let's do it. (Yes, sir).

Not to play stewardess or anything but. . . "Please keep your arms and legs in the vehicle at all times." And, here we go. . . 10. . . 9. . . 8. . . 7. . . 6. . . 5 . . .4. . . 3 . . .2. . . 1 . . . WOOOOOOOOOOSH!. . . (perfect launch, sir). . . OK, whatever.

It was like no time had elapsed at all when Fred could hear the booming sound of the crowds chanting and clapping. Oh, this is what Fred was waiting for. All of this was in his honor! Fred tried to hold this moment in mental freeze frame, but, alas, nothing lasts forever. There would need to be another and another. . . and another mission to feel this good again.

Fred could hear nothing from the outside world. Only this world within his own imagination brought such treasures. It would be hard to leave this world again. But the outside world had very stringent demands and didn't like to be kept waiting! Fred must return.

CHAPTER SIX

Fred began missing his chain whenever they were apart. Its allure was becoming stronger and stronger with each passing day. At night, when they were alone together again, Fred would have some pretty intimate talks with this bracketed friend. They could talk for hours (the chain mostly listened). Fred never heard a harsh word from his companion. This was an attachment that was completely predictable, completely controllable, and completely captivated. The chain never seemed to mind when Fred would go on for hours about what his day was like or how he was feeling. He was never laughed at, never rejected, and never abandoned. They were so close and Fred needed to feel close to something.

Most of Fred's evenings were rather quiet and undisturbed,

but this particular evening would be neither. Fred had just said goodnight to his faithful friend when he heard the most frightening sound. It was coming from a tent farther away but it sounded like it was heading straight at him.

Egbert seemed to be aging far too quickly. He would hardly eat. It was no secret to all the circus crew that Egbert would throw frequent bizarre fits with the collateral damage getting more and more severe with each episode. Normally, the staff was able to provide a secure perimeter for the mysterious spells, but this time, Egbert broke through. In what seemed like fractions of a second, Egbert had pummeled into Fred's tent and stopped just short of Fred's quivering nose. Fred couldn't focus on the multitude of approaching intervening footsteps. The only thing he saw and heard was the monstrous body of a rageful enigma apparently intent on scaring him to death. . . (and it was working!). Fred remained in his submissive position hoping that would calm this thing down. . . (but that didn't seem to be working).

The rescue personnel did arrive but not before Egbert released the enitre content of his built up venom on his shattered son. Egbert wanted to make sure Fred knew who he was, but not for any compassionate reason. Egbert wanted Fred to face the "victim" of his selfish murderous son's act.

"He hates me?". . . "He doesn't want to be my father?". . . "He hopes I die for what I did?". . . "I killed my mother?"

Fred was too shocked to take it all in or to process any of

what he had just heard. But, his questions continued.

"I have a father. . . and he doesn't want me?". . . "I'm so awful that I killed my own mother?" "What kind of a son makes his father hate him that much?". . . "Isn't a father suppposed to love you?". . . "How can anyone else ever want me if my own father doesn't?". . . "Aren't people who kill other people supposed to die?"

Fred couldn't think anymore. He felt as if he was dead, at least on the inside.

Egbert was finally removed and led back to his own tent. No one seemed to notice the look on Fred's face. No one seemed to notice. . . or care. . . that a little soul seemed to die that day. Egbert, on the other hand got lots of attention and words of concern and comfort. Could this be more "evidence" that Fred really was the bad guy and that his pain had no cause, or at least, deserved no attention. Fred's tent was left in shambles. Compared to the overwhelming internal damage to one small elephant; however, the superficial destruction could be deemed to be trivial.

Although so tired and confused, Fred tried to make sense out of all that had just happened. The only conclusion he could come up with was that familiar theme of horrendous shame and guilt. There was loss, too, but Fred couldn't imagine how a culpable inmate had the right to believe that any of that loss mattered now.

Fred lay frozen in his familiar confines for quite some

time before he could begin to rest for the night. Fred braved one thought about the mother Egbert spoke of. Somehow Fred began to remember hearing her voice a long time ago, but something strange happenned. Then the voice just stopped.

Fred wondered, "Does she hate me too?"

Fred knew that deep down he really missed her, but he probably didn't even deserve to do that. No tears came that day. They were banished to the inner resources of secret keeping. Fred simply instinctively searched for his chain and rested his head over it for safe keeping.

Fred didn't travel much after that day. The grateful crowd, he at one time longed for, now felt like a cruel kick in the gut. He no longer believed he deserved any kind of honor, worth or value. He didn't want to be exalted. He wanted to be annihilated. He needed to hurt. He needed to pay for all that he had done. . . for all he was . . . for being born at all. Fred did not know how to face these feelings. To him, these monstrous emotions were too vicious to be acknowledged. They were the new enemy.

CHAPTER SEVEN

Fred was growing from head to. . . ankle. . . to toe. To make things worse, this was occurring behind his back and beyond his control. His frame was expanding. The first clue to the clueless owner was Fred's blanket. Mysteriously, this nighttime cover was becoming an ever-diminishing asset. The annoying outcome was Fred's having to face those chilly sunsets with less than adequate personal coverage.

But Fred's struggles didn't stop there. Not only did Fred awaken to those devious drafts, sometimes the sleeping interruption came in the form of disturbances farther south. It never failed, one false turn in the foot's flipping over and there was pain to pay. Right about where the ankle ring and the chain met, there was a pound of flesh in jeopardy. Fred never seemed to have this kind of trouble before, and this particular pang seemed intent on getting Fred's attention.

Although Fred had become quite seasoned at pain management, especially when it came to wounds of the heart, physical pain just didn't seem to register as quite as threatening. In fact, as Fred deliberated on this frequent onslaught, there was a curious release or relief experienced from each episode. Ever since Fred concluded that he was not about to let those vulnerable feelings out, the only sensation left was the haunting residual of *numb*. After a while Fred had to admit that the state of *numb* had its own tortures. And maybe, just maybe, this might be the answer Fred was looking for.

Could there even be a bonus package included in this new discovery here? Fred had also noticed that this same sharp sting gave him the needed assurance that, in some way, he actually could feel alive.

The clincher, and final selling point, was that sense of long past due judgment he could enact upon himself. How fitting this pain would be, applied directly and punitively to the comprehensively *guilty*. And *guilty* was that overriding conviction Fred bathed in at every turn. Fred marveled as he pondered the myriad of opportunities laid, literally, at his feet.

This was it, the beginning of a riveting relationship with pain. It would distract, deliver and demean. It would offer so much, but demand even more. It would fail to satiate, but prove to enslave. Yet, options seemed limited, and Fred's intimate friend was now allowed to provide Fred a way to avoid and survive. Fred had lost hope for any freedom or peace for himself and his future.

This accidental discovery soon became a daily ritual. For all intents and purposes, Fred hung on to this behavior as the perceived miracle medicine. . . I wonder if anyone would notice the scars. . . Fred doubted it.

CHAPTER EIGHT

Fred had it all figured out. Circus life was far from attractive, but it certainly was predictable. No one likes surprises, at least not the kind Fred had grown used to expecting. He was finally starting to feel like he was in the driver's seat, even if the cruise control was always on.

Despite Fred's plans, however, change was on its way and life would take a turn toward the unknown. The announcement came one drizzly morning as Fred overheard the conversation outside his tent, a conversation between the circus director and a local businessman. Fred's jaw dropped to the floor when he discovered he was to be transferred.

"Transferred!"

Fred was approaching near hysteria! Fred tried to make

sense of this shocking bulletin. . . "Isn't *transferred* remotely akin to CHANGE?!". . .

"I don't **DO** change. . . I don't **LIKE** change. . . I don't **KNOW** change. . . I don't **TRUST** change. . . and I don't **WANT** it!!"

How silly it was to assume that Fred would actually get any say in the matter. There was, of course, already a contract signed and sealed. Fred could only decipher a word here and there, but not enough to make any sense out of any additional details. Fred strained to try and hear at least where he was going, but all he could grasp was the sound of laughter as the businessman was saying something about Fred's new surroundings. Fred was determined to stay and listen until all was revealed, but no sooner did the laughter cease than the two gentlemen were called away to the business office.

Fred was in shock. He couldn't move. . . He stood frozen. . . waiting. . . hoping that he might have misunderstood. . . maybe they weren't really talking about him. . . maybe this was all a big bad dream. . . maybe he would turn into his father and **LOSE IT**. . . maybe he wanted to.

All Fred could do was wait. Fred stopped eating. His stomach was swirling in acrobatic sommersaults. His room started spinning. Fred wasn't even sure if he was breathing anymore, but that didn't really matter either.

Days passed until Fred knew more.

"Rockwood Zoo?. . . OK. . . not too familiar with the 'zoo'

thing. . . uh boy!" All Fred had known was circus life and chained solitude.

"So, what in the world am I supposed to do there?". . . "Do I get my own tent?". . . "Of course my sturdy roommate will be going along," Fred surmised, but this was not to be. For, in that day of transition, his friend was taken off and away, and Fred was led on to the moving trailer never to see his friend again.

Shaking in disbelief, Fred drew to the corner of the compartment and stared into empty space.

"Now what?!" he cried.

CHAPTER NINE

The trailer ride seemed to go on forever. Fred was not very thrilled with all the bumps and swaying. His stomach was already in a mess, and his mind wasn't far behind.

Fred wondered what life would be like. He wondered why he had to leave the circus in the first place. He wondered what he had done to be sent away like this. There were no easy answers. . . no answers really. Fred just knew he hated leaving. . . having to start all over again.

Fred was unaware that "different" could be better than "same." What he was aware of was that "same" felt better, and he was not happy with any of this!

After hours on the road, Fred began to get very sleepy. His eyes became too heavy to continue his nervous gaze. The next thing Fred knew the trailer had stopped. Startled by the clanging of metal and the loud voices, Fred realized he had reached his destination. It was dark outside and it didn't smell the same. Fred slowly exited the vehicle and gingerly descended down the ramp to the ground below.

There it was, this huge sign welcoming him to the Rockwood Zoo. As Fred approached the entrance his heart began to flutter.

"What is going to happen to me?" he squealed. . . "I wonder what the trainers are like here?" "I wonder what they were told about me?". . . "Will they hate me, too?". . . "Maybe it will be okay if I just don't let them get too close!"

Fred was still groggy from his long trip and just wanted to rest. Maybe it was all just a dream, (and if that was the case, Fred resolved to abstain from any more weighty late evening snacks right before bedtime. . . It was the chain's idea. . .). Maybe he would wake up tomorrow and be back in his own tent and back with his friend.

CHAPTER TEN

The morning came and Fred opened his eyes to find out he had not been dreaming. . . he was not back in his tent. Rather, he found himself curled up between two **HUGE** boulders. The weather that day was cloudy and the sky was darker than usual. Visibility was hampered. Fred, for several hours, hadn't even noticed that he was not alone. He just assumed. . .

Not only was Fred not in his tent, he was confounded by the realization that he was being stared at by a crowd of onlookers.

"OK. . . **Who** are all these people. . . and **Why** are they staring at me?!" Fred exclaimed.

"I am **SURE** it's too early for show time, and I haven't even had my breakfast yet!". . . "OK, there's a fence there, that's good". . . "**What** in tarnation are they throwing at me?". . . "peanuts?". . . "not exacly what I had in mind". . . "So, how long does thing go on, anyway?". . . "Yes! They're leaving"

. . . "So long!". . . "Miss you!". . . "and uh, don't let the door hit you on the way out!". . . "Oh - for crying out loud - there's more!"

Fred couldn't believe it. All day long, people just came to watch him do. . .nothing. There were no performances, practices, or petrified participants. . . and no pressure to present the perfect show. He could just be . . .himself. . . ("If they really knew me," Fred conjectured. . . "they would run for the hills!").

About midday, Fred became curious regarding his new surroundings and had the subtle twinge to do some exploring. But, Fred had become accustomed to stationary living quarters and quickly stifled the intruding proposal. The world out there had never been too kind. . .

"Let's just play it safe, shall we!," was the motto Fred had relied on for quite some time.

The clouds began to lift and Fred's domestic abode was becoming more and more clear. Not only was his crash pad getting clearer by the moment, it was also getting more and more crowded by the moment!

"What's this. . . neighbors?. . . Oh NO!. . . Somebody, please tell me this is not happening! (uh. . . never mind on the 'Somebody please tell me' part!)". . .

Fred was quite attached to the loner lifestyle and was far from interested in any form of *group bonding*. Isolating with his old personified companion had been a *soothing balm* that served a necessary purpose on so many levels, that Fred was not about to dismiss what seemed to be *helping*. Besides, Fred was really starting to miss his old companion and wasn't much in the mood for socializing!

CHAPTER ELEVEN

Apparently, no one else got the "I don't want to talk to you" memo and everyone was eagerly on his or her way to meet the new arrival. Fred had to admit, it was kinda nice to be around people who looked like him. At the same time, it felt strange.

All of a sudden, Fred felt overwhelming panic at the sight of a large male approaching. Fred couldn't understand why he was having such a strong reaction to this complete stranger.

All he knew was that everything/everyone inside of him was screaming, "Run!"

It's unclear how the word *run* got translated from the mind to the body as *freeze*, nevertheless, that's exactly what Fred did.

No doubt, to the confused onlooker, Fred's posed portrait resembled something like the world's largest frozen animal popsicle. Fred just couldn't move. . . (and "acting natural" was definetly out of the question). So, Fred *bravely* met the eager callers with eyes open with a somewhat ridiculous-looking strained smile on his face.

Thankfully, no one seemed to care about first impressions and everyone greeted Fred with sincere interest. Gratefully, Fred was then immediately *saved* by the dinner bell as his new acquaintances reacted in the instinctual herd mindset aiming straight for the meal trough. Fred remained at the end of the line berating himself in every way possible for "*obviously* looking so **Stupid**!"

Strangely, not so far behind this self-bashing internal scrutiny, came a revelation that, at least now, maybe they would all stay away from him since he had shown himself to be so undoubtedly and undeniably undesirable! This conclusion he was sure was best for their sakes as well as his.

CHAPTER TWELVE

The next morning brought even more surprises and Fred was becoming increasingly resistant to all the things that seemed so far out of his comfort zone of the known.

Fred heard something. . . footsteps. . . smaller footsteps than his counterparts.

"A trainer, maybe," Fred thought.

As Fred turned his head in the direction of the sounds, he saw a man coming toward him with a bag in his hand. Fred quickly ruled out peanuts. . . it just wasn't the peanut carrying kind of bag. Fred wouldn't have minded peanuts, though; he was a little hungry.

Despite his hunger, Fred remained pretty apprehensive and felt his body automatically recoil slightly. To his astonishment, this "doctor" empathetically observed Fred's anxiety and responded in a nurturing and understanding way. He was not demanding or critical. Nor was he in need of constant pacifying. Fred didn't know how to take this.

Before too long, the doctor noticed the scarred ankle and proceeded to dress it and then write something on his writing pad. Whatever the doctor did made it feel better in the end, but Fred still wasn't sure if he wanted or even deserved that. The doctor spoke kindly to Fred, and then went on his way.

Fred was becoming more and more perplexed with the "different" thing, but he was sure of one thing. He still didn't trust it!

Fred sat for a while contemplating his bandaged ankle. He was having plenty of urges to rip that bandage right off. . . but he wasn't really ready for that either.

EPILOGUE

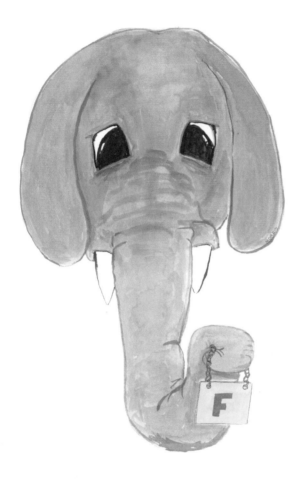

    Fred had many more "different" experiences while at Rockwood Zoo, and many of them he fought tooth and nail. Over time, he would try the patience of some, alienate others, and trust a few. But for Fred, this was a hopeful beginning.

    It wouldn't be easy, and some days would just be *horrible*. Along the way, though, Fred would be given opportunities to review his life and challenge some beliefs he had drawn from what had happened that were no longer useful.

He was in the right place to choose to live and to heal, and this time it was totally up to him.

The *FRED'S STORY*
Workbook

A pdf copy of this workbook can be downloaded
without charge and used without further
permission from www.rossinst.com.

CHAPTER ONE

Fred's parents were influenced by their family history and culture. When "it's always been done that way," the "it" is often accepted as the normal, accepted and best.

- What were some of the passed down "norms" or "rules" you witnessed or experienced in your family?

_____

_____

_____

_____

_____

_____

_____

_____

_____

_____

_____

Fred's parents had an attachment with their ancestors and had a desire to conform

and belong. Compliance seemed to be the key
protection against rejection and isolation.

- **What were some of the consequences
  or fears in your family related to being
  perceived as "disloyal" in thinking or
  behavior?**

_____

_____

_____

_____

_____

_____

_____

_____

_____

_____

Fred's parents had a common case
of ambivalent feelings about doing things
differently than what was expected and
accepted. And, there was the assumption that
these internal struggles would automatically
resolve if a geographical cure was applied.

However, Fred's parents discovered that neither the death of others nor physical separation from them would stop the emotional conflict.

- In what ways have you tried to convince yourself that this kind of struggle within no longer exists?

_____

_____

_____

_____

_____

_____

_____

_____

_____

_____

_____

- What evidence is there that the struggle is still affecting you?

_____

_____

_____

_____

_____

_____

_____

_____

_____

_____

_____

_____

Fred's mother experienced some of the physical effects of emotional distress. Bessel A. van der Kolk wrote that, "The Body Keeps the Score."

- Using the "B" alliteration below for the areas or systems often affected by patterns of stress and emotional pain, list the symptoms you have had or are experiencing that may be related to your trauma.

Brain: _____

_____

_____

_____

_____

Bones: _____

_____

_____

_____

_____

Belly:_____

_____

_____

_____

_____

Bowels:_____

_____

_____

_____

_____

Breather:_____

_____

_____

_____

_____

Beater: _____

_____

_____

_____

_____

Blood Pressure:_____

_____

_____

_____

CHAPTER TWO

Fred's father blamed him for two things, even though Fred didn't have control over either one. Fred was blamed for *the death of his mother* and for *being born*. When something benign precedes something tragic, the benign is sometimes blamed in an attempt to pinpoint a cause of the tragedy. Then, while in severe pain, a suffering one sometimes demands an answer when none is currently available. Unable or unwilling to accept feelings of being out of control or vulnerable, an "answer" is wrongly assigned.

- How have you been blamed for the tragedies and/or traumas in your life?

_____

_____

_____

_____

_____

_____

_____

_____

_____

_____

_____

Fred's father spent a very brief period questioning his own culpability in his mate's death. His initial theory was that the "all seeing eyes of the ages" were able to both detect and punish one who was disobedient. It is also apparent that this enforcer's retribution was disproportionate to the "crime" as well as being merciless.

- In response to perceived infractions,when and how have you assigned yourself consequences that were both overly-critical and cruel to yourself?

_____

_____

_____

_____

_____

_____

_____

_____

_____

_____

_____

_____

Fred's father quickly dismisses this hypothesis, believing that he could not fathom or tolerate in any way being connected to the loss of his beloved. From here he engages in *projection:* seeing in another the "evil" he fears or cannot own in himself.

- When and how have you been blamed for the guilt (true or false) others were unwilling to address within themselves?

_____

_____

_____

_____

_____

_____

_____

_____

_____

_____

_____

- When and how have you acted out the guilt and shame belonging to others?

_____

_____

_____

_____

_____

_____

_____

_____

_____

_____

Fred's growing years would be replete with unwanted occurrences. These would be painful. Deeper and more complex, however, would be the wounds resulting from what did *not* occur.

- What are some of these pervasive unmet needs that you have brought with you into your adult years?

_____

Peace

Love

Approval

Acceptance

Protection

Nurturing

Support

Celebration

Encouragement

Companionship

Boundaries

Autonomy

Individuation

Comfort

Security

CHAPTER THREE

Fred's introduction to captivity was not by choice. He was bearing the consequences for others' behaviors.

- In what ways have you had to suffer for the infractions of others?

_____

_____

_____

_____

_____

_____

_____

_____

Fred was not happy with his new chains. No doubt he yanked and yanked on them for quite some time. Eventually, when no amount of effort worked, and no one came to rescue, Fred realized how useless and painful it was trying to make things change or experience freedom. So he stopped fighting. Helplessness is learned. Captivity is chosen, surrendered to, in order to block the pain of hope which always seemed to lead to disappointment.

- **What are the areas in your life in which you currently feel helpless?**

_____

_____

_____

_____

_____

_____

_____

_____

_____

_____

_____

- **Where do you think you first learned this helpless mindset?**

_____

_____

_____

_____

_____

_____

_____

_____

_____

_____

_____

Fred's learned helplessness led to an attachment to the state of captivity. The enemy was now ingeniously turned into an ally. Fred did not have the opportunity to become bonded to his mother as he desperately needed. She was with him for a while, but then she was just gone. Fred could not survive without something to cling to that he could call _his_. In the absence of the ideal, make-shift substitutes are often created. Fred would

attach to an object. It was always there when he needed it.

- When people weren't there for you, what replacement(s) did you turn to for security? (Some of these things may be those familiar things you haven't let go of yet.)

_____

_____

_____

_____

_____

_____

_____

_____

_____

_____

_____

- What are the things you may still be holding on to that now have become your way of avoiding connection with others?

_____

_____

_____

_____

_____

_____

_____

_____

_____

_____

_____

_____

CHAPTER FOUR

Fred had nearly reached the point of despair trying to please his trainer "at least once." Contributing to this kind of despair are the following *false* assumptions/beliefs:

- The one he was trying to please was willing and able to be pleased.

  (Assumed goodness/willingness)

- The one he was trying to please was being *forced* to be unhappy due to Fred's imperfect performance.

  (External locus of control)

- The one he was trying to please would *have* to be happy if Fred could just do it right.

  (Cause and effect thinking)

- The one he was trying to please was confirming that Fred must be bad because he kept doing something wrong.

  (Being = doing)

**Which of these false assumptions relate most
to you? How have they affected you in the
past? How are they affecting your life now?**

_____

_____

_____

_____

_____

_____

_____

_____

_____

_____

_____

_____

**Fred's introduction into circus life
was an intense lesson that, in some social
dynamics, it is considered "awful" for those
under us to make mistakes. The "house rule"
is, "Make me look good!" as if you are merely a
reflection of them. Sometimes extreme reactions
are displayed either when the "reflection" is
perceived to have tainted the image of the
narcissist, or when the "reflection" is being**

acclaimed for his/her *own* accomplishment and praise seems to be withheld from the narcissist for his/her *perceived* contribution.

- Can you identify any of these types of individuals in your past or present? How have you been affected by their influence?

_____

_____

_____

_____

_____

_____

_____

_____

_____

_____

_____

Fred's strategic thinking, after repeated disappointments with trying to gain the approval of his trainer, might have deduced that this endeavor was both futile and impossible. So, Fred could have taken one or more of these approaches to the option of "trying."

- "Do nothing." "It's just not worth the effort. . . and if I don't try, I can't be evaluated."

- "Do as little as possible." "It won't be enough whatever I do . . . but at least they can't say I didn't try." "Just do enough to get by."

- "Do something to sabotage it." "I need a good excuse for not performing well." "That way, it won't look as bad."

- "Do it 110% all the time." "I've got something to prove . . . I'll show them I'm not a failure!"

- "Do it only if you can guarantee success." "Do only what you do well. . . avoid all risk of failure. . . it's about winning not enjoying"

- "Do it better than the rest." "I can't let myself or others know how inferior I feel. . . the best mask against this is to appear as superior."

- "Do your own criticizing and self-punishing." Better to be in control of the time, method and severity of the *lashing* than to leave it to others."

- "Do the world a favor and withdraw." They don't need you in there trying, messing up the works. Nobody needs failures around." (The "bad guy" finds a way to be the "good guy.")

Describe how you have used these strategies in your own life. Identify the perceived "pay offs."

_____

_____

_____

_____

_____

_____

_____

_____

_____

_____

_____

_____

_____

_____

CHAPTER FIVE

Fred was gifted with a creative mind, which came in handy during those rough days and long lonely nights. For Fred, the world of reality continued to feel very foreign to him, and he wanted a world of his own. It seemed to Fred that the external world was neither safe nor accepting. That world could not be controlled or manipulated. On the contrary, the inside world could not be breached and it did not need to be escaped. The possibilities in this world extended as far as the imagination could take them. These dissociative rituals began quite automatically at first, but Fred was quick to realize their disconnecting powers.   Before too long, he became quite adept at setting up the flight sequence.

- Childhood is the period of the *open window* for imaginative play and thinking. Here lies the optimal potential for the development of dissociative patterns. What were the traumas in your past where these coping maneuvers first began? Describe the ways you were able to "check

**out" when the external world became too
threatening:**

_____

_____

_____

_____

_____

_____

_____

_____

_____

_____

_____

_____

_____

_____

_____

_____

_____

_____

_____

_____

Fred would illustrate how dissociative behaviors are prone to become increasingly automatic to the exclusion of other forms of coping. Once the benefits of the behavior are experienced, survivors often learn to use this skill at will. Dissociation is a creative and necessary adaptation during the original period of trauma. Then, survival was the only priority. Now, this same skill can actually result in negative consequences of increased vulnerability, unhealthy forms of disconnection, and a deterioration of other coping abilities.

- From your own history, describe your tendencies to withdraw and escape mentally. How has the overuse of this coping skill now become ineffective or counterproductive?

_____

_____

_____

_____

_____

_____

CHAPTER SIX

Fred was having a fantasy affair with his chain. He could pretend it was exactly the "person" he wanted it to be. It would have no expectations, would never get upset, and would like everything about him. It was a no-risk relationship. Fred could ignore what it really was and remain fixated on what he thought it was. He just needed to have someone. . . something.

- What past or current relationships have you convinced yourself were better than they actually were? What or who do these people remind you of from your past? Is there a common pattern in these relationships, whether in the traits of people you are attracted to, or in the way you interact in these relationships?

_____

_____

_____

_____

_____

_____

Fred's father had become consumed in his own misery. Although a true victim of horrendous loss, he had become clouded in self-absorption. Self-care was absent, premature aging was present, and his moods were becoming more and more unstable to the point of severe bouts of violence.

- From your childhood, how was the expression of anger modeled for you? What are your learned beliefs regarding your own anger and the anger of others? What are the symptoms or evidence that your anger is not being managed or expressed in healthy ways?

_____

_____

_____

_____

_____

_____

_____

_____

_____

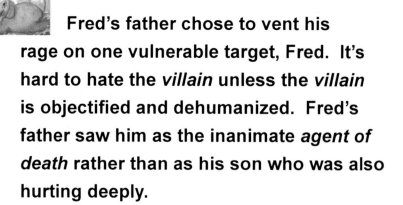 Fred's father chose to vent his rage on one vulnerable target, Fred. It's hard to hate the *villain* unless the *villain* is objectified and dehumanized. Fred's father saw him as the inanimate *agent of death* rather than as his son who was also hurting deeply.

- How has a lack of empathy with yourself or someone else contributed to your acting out in anger on yourself or someone else?

_____

_____

_____

_____

_____

_____

_____

_____

_____

_____

_____

_____

_____

_____

_____

_____

_____

_____

_____

_____

_____

_____

_____

_____

_____

Fred heard some very painful announcements and/or lies from his father. He was too small to understand the fallacies in his father's words. What Fred heard that day led to some commonly held misbeliefs accepted by many trauma survivors.

- **Challenge these common thinking errors with reality based truth**

Misbelief	Truth
"My existence has hurt others"	
"If my parents didn't love me, no one else can."	
"I'm responsible for what was out of my control."	
"I deserve to die for what happened."	

Misbelief	Truth
"I am awful, bad."	
"I make other people hate and hurt me."	
"I could have stopped what happened."	
"I deserve what happened."	

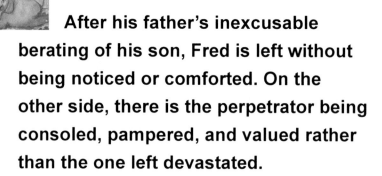 **After his father's inexcusable berating of his son, Fred is left without being noticed or comforted. On the other side, there is the perpetrator being consoled, pampered, and valued rather than the one left devastated.**

- **How do you relate to this kind of experience? How have you tried to make sense of it? How has this betrayal and abandonment affected you?**

_____

_____

_____

_____

_____

_____

_____

_____

_____

_____

_____

_____

This was a day Fred decided he didn't deserve to feel any of his emotions of loss and, again, traded the feelings of grief for shame and guilt. He minimized his pain and maximized his self-loathing. He turned off the faucet for his tears and sought protection from his feelings rather than healing for his pain.

- How do you "feel" about your feelings? Do you allow some to surface but avoid others? What thoughts or beliefs contribute to how you relate with your own emotions? _____

_____

_____

_____

_____

_____

_____

_____

_____

_____

_____

CHAPTER SEVEN

Fred was certainly out of touch with how his body was changing. Growing up. . . and out. . . he was getting bigger than he used to be, yet, the child within was ever-present. Chronologically, he was advancing, but emotionally he was stunted due to uncompleted developmental accomplishments.

• As you look in the mirror, do you see someone who is not a child anymore? Yet, at times, do you feel like anything but an adult? Describe your current struggles with the parts of you that are still trying to *catch up* emotionally.

_____

_____

_____

_____

_____

_____

_____

_____

_____

_____

_____

_____

_____

_____

_____

_____

_____

_____

_____

_____

_____

_____

_____

_____

_____

_____

_____

For Fred, the present seemed distorted by the revelation of child parts within. In the past, there existed another distortion. He would look at the past and judge his history as if he were an adult at the time and had insight or responsibilities

that he really could *not* have had at that
time. He would label himself as guilty,
selfish, stupid, and irresponsible, based on
this unfair measuring stick.

- How have you judged your current or past
  behavior unfairly due to this sense of
  "always being the adult?"

_____

_____

_____

_____

_____

_____

_____

_____

_____

_____

_____

_____

_____

_____

_____

_____

_____

_____

_____

_____

_____

_____

_____

_____

_____

_____

_____

_____

_____

_____

_____

_____

_____

Fred discovers the "coping skill" of self-injury, sabotaging the opportunity to be in touch with the feelings he fears or hates. His feelings have become the *enemy, when the actual enemies are* the painful lies he has chosen to believe in light of his many heart wounds.

How are each of the following rationales for self-harm detrimental to your recovery? What are more healthy alternatives for emotional expression and regulation?

- *Redirect* emotional pain to "less threatening" physical pain:

_____

_____

_____

_____

_____

_____

- *Re-enact* the abuse you experienced:

_____

_____

_____

_____

_____

_____

- *Release* pent up energy or anxiety:

_____

_____

_____

_____

_____

- *Render* a punitive sense of justice/judgment against self for *perceived* wrongs:

_____

_____

_____

_____

_____

_____

- *Relieve* experiences of being emotionally *numb* or *dead*:

_____

_____

_____

_____

_____

_____

CHAPTER EIGHT

Fred wasn't under the illusion that the life he had grown accustomed to was "all that good." But, it *was* predictable. Fred wasn't choosing a bad option over a good one. There was no doubt. . . in his mind. . . that the only two options available for him were *bad* and most likely *worse*. His decision seemed to make sense to him and his history. He would whine about his predicament periodically, but that didn't mean he was planning on going anywhere else.

• Although recovery is an opportunity to start moving out of the "pit," sometimes we choose to just decorate the pit rather than put up a "for sale" sign. This is the "ambivalence" every survivor struggles with, and it is an important part of recovery to "count the cost" of the move. What are your current fears about the "move" including those things you may have to give up or leave behind? There may also be some "good" things that may be lost in search of the "better" or "best."

Fred did NOT like anything about the word *CHANGE*. Even "good" change (*not that Fred believed there was such a thing*) was HARD! Change means starting over. . . moving out of automatic drive into manual. The brain craves repetition and is all too willing to create short-cuts for us when a pattern has been detected. Before the pattern is detected, however, the "good" changes that have been begun just don't instantly start to *feel* good.

- What are some new positive habits you are willing to pursue, knowing that the transition phase will involve facing and processing your issues of ambivalence?

_____

_____

_____

_____

_____

_____

_____

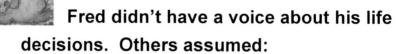 Fred didn't have a voice about his life decisions. Others assumed:

- he didn't deserve a say

- he didn't want to have to say

- he didn't have anything *worthwhile* to say

- he couldn't be understood (he *was* an elephant)

- In what way has your life felt controlled by others? In what ways have you allowed others to control you? What are some beliefs you hold that may be contributing to your choice to not be assertive?

_____

_____

_____

_____

_____

_____

_____

_____

_____

_____

_____

Fred got very panicky about the move and even doubted his own ability to "keep it together." Fred had his father's legacy of "lack of control," and Fred feared that his father's genes might take over at any point.

- How has the fear of "turning into my parents" given false credence to some of your helplessness/hopelessness beliefs?

_____

_____

_____

_____

_____

_____

_____

_____

_____

_____

_____

CHAPTER NINE

Fred's ride to his new zoo home was *unpleasant*. Fred wasn't a real fan of bumpy roads and motion sickness, but he was less of a fan when it came to the idea of change. Fred struggled to categorize the opportunity of change in anything other than a negative frame. He saw it as frightening as well as a possible punishment for bad behavior.

- How have you labeled and responded to the possibilities of change and/or new starts in your life?

_____

_____

_____

_____

_____

_____

_____

_____

_____

_____

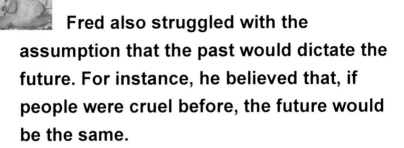 Fred also struggled with the assumption that the past would dictate the future. For instance, he believed that, if people were cruel before, the future would be the same.

- How has your adopted "life script" of *negative future likelihoods* interfered with some potential positive options for you?

_____

_____

_____

_____

_____

_____

_____

_____

_____

_____

_____

_____

_____

_____

CHAPTER TEN

Fred's nightly rituals of preferred privacy with his chain buddy were no longer available. Fred was now confronted with way more transparency than he wanted. There could be no more hiding. As far as Fred was concerned, these new onlookers were just *in his space.*

- Describe your level of comfort when you are in social situations. In what ways is transparency undesirable for you?

_____

_____

_____

_____

_____

_____

_____

_____

_____

_____

_____

Fred became perplexed at the realization that his audience wasn't interested in any staged performances. Although a relief in some aspects, this increased closeness created anxiety for Fred who feared his "worthlessness" would be that much more easily detected.

- How has closeness to others been a trigger for you, creating some unhealthy reactions based on fear and shame?

_____

_____

_____

_____

_____

_____

_____

_____

_____

_____

_____

_____

Fred must have muttered, "And the hits just keep on coming!" when the increased visibility revealed that he wasn't the only one on his side of the fence. He was already missing his old friend and didn't want to feel any more *salt in the wound* by having to open up to anyone else.

- There's often an uncomfortable transition phase encountered when you are confronted with the presence of mutual companionship when all you've felt safe with before was some replacement for true peer intimacy. How have you developed patterns of emotional or physical isolation when responding to feelings of "loneliness" or "rejection" in social situations? What are your triggers or beliefs that lead to your choices to isolate?

_____

_____

_____

_____

CHAPTER ELEVEN

Fred was surprised to witness people who seemed to be happy to see and meet him. The positive words and gestures seemed nice, but they just felt too strange to be good, *Fred thought*.

- How do you respond to the positive strokes you receive from others? How do you block or discount them?

_____

_____

_____

_____

_____

_____

_____

_____

_____

_____

_____

_____

_____

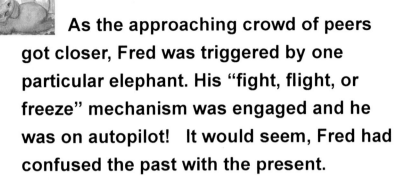 As the approaching crowd of peers got closer, Fred was triggered by one particular elephant. His "fight, flight, or freeze" mechanism was engaged and he was on autopilot!   It would seem, Fred had confused the past with the present.

- How do you tend to confuse the past with the present as you react to certain people or troublesome situations?

_____

_____

_____

_____

_____

_____

_____

_____

_____

_____

_____

_____

_____

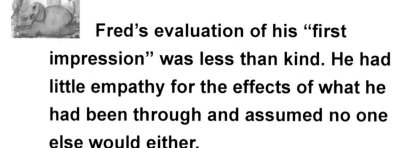 Fred's evaluation of his "first impression" was less than kind. He had little empathy for the effects of what he had been through and assumed no one else would either.

- How do the standards you hold for yourself sometimes not take into account what you have been through and the impact it has had on your life? How do you tend to judge yourself when you notice you are struggling in some area?

_____

_____

_____

_____

_____

_____

_____

_____

_____

_____

_____

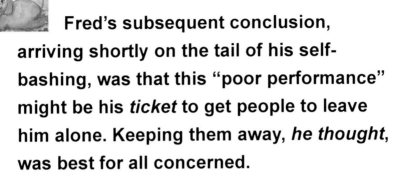 Fred's subsequent conclusion, arriving shortly on the tail of his self-bashing, was that this "poor performance" might be his *ticket* to get people to leave him alone. Keeping them away, *he thought*, was best for all concerned.

- How have you sabotaged certain interactions with others in a subtle attempt to create more of a *safe* distance?

_____

_____

_____

_____

_____

_____

_____

_____

_____

_____

_____

_____

_____

CHAPTER TWELVE

Fred's encounter with the zoo doctor introduced some new relational dynamics to the table. Nevertheless, it brought some initial caution and mistrust toward such an *unknown* guest. Fred couldn't help noticing that this bag-carrying man did not resort to anger, nor did he require emotional pampering.

- How have the relational roles of perpetrator-victim-rescuer been embedded in your mind as evidenced by how you relate with others? How comfortable do you feel when more healthy patterns are offered?

_____

_____

_____

_____

_____

_____

_____

_____

_____

Fred had mixed emotions about the doctor's caring ways. He did cling to his "undeserving" personal assessment. At the same time, for the *first* time, he was able to question whether or not he was as fond of the old way as he was before.

- Describe this similar kind of ambivalence pattern in your own life?

_____

_____

_____

_____

_____

_____

_____

_____

_____

_____

_____

_____

_____

EPILOGUE

What are some of the most important or significant discoveries, insights, and decisions you have made while reading and processing *Fred's Story*.

_____

_____

_____

_____

_____

_____

_____

_____

_____

_____

_____

_____

_____

_____

_____

_____

_____

_____

NOTES _____

_____

_____

_____

_____

_____

_____

_____

_____

_____

_____

_____

_____

_____

_____

_____

_____

_____

_____

_____

_____

_____

_____

_____